DON'T YOU TURN BACK

DON'T YOU

TURN BACK

Poems by LANGSTON HUGHES

Selected by Lee Bennett Hopkins

Woodcuts by Ann Grifalconi

Alfred A. Knopf · New York

An Introduction by Arna Bontemps

He seemed too young. Actually Langston Hughes was going on twenty-three, and he had just returned from long voyages to seaports around Europe and down the coast of West Africa. He had been working as a merchant seaman for about two years, and along the way he had stopped in Paris long enough to get a job as a dishwasher in a cabaret, go sight-seeing in Spain and Italy, and write a notebookful of new poems on land and on shipboard. Many of the poems he had just written are included in this book, along with others selected from ones he had written earlier and which I had read in magazines.

We met at the apartment of a young librarian and her roommate, who was a secretary to an editor at the time. Before the evening was over, Langston reached into his pocket, brought out his notebook, and read a number of his new poems to us. Already we were all his fans, but that night we became his friends. Forty years later he died in New York, and what shocked those who had known him a long time was that he still seemed too young.

It was after he had written and published two books of his poems that librarians and teachers first seemed to realize that the quality of youngness was in the poems themselves as well as in his person-ality, and it was not long until many young readers formed the same opinion.

Now that there have been many more books by Langston Hughes, many more poems from which to make a selection, and another genera-tion of young people are ready for poetry that speaks to them in a special way, it is good to have a new collection of his easy-to-remember, hard-to-forget, sensitively illustrated poems presented to young readers. Such a book is a treasure they will want to keep.

To me it is a reminder of a little poem he once wrote to me instead of a letter. I had asked him to send me some poems for a collection I

was making for young readers in the years soon after we met. He sent
a large selection, and these lines accompanied them:

May 31,1941

Dear Arna,
  Some of these for children,
  And some for older fry,
  You may take your choice
  Since you're as old as I.
            Sincerely,
              Lang

CONTENTS

My People

Prayers and Dreams

Out to Sea

I Am A Negro

A Note from the Editor

In June, 1967, one month after the death of Langston Hughes, a poetry-memorial was held to honor this great poet; the testimony to a man and his work was presented by a group of fourth graders in New York's Harlem. The poems were chosen by the youngsters themselves. Their teacher had expressed doubt as to whether or not the children would appreciate Mr. Hughes' adult words and images. The children proved that his words were meant for them, too.

Langston Hughes' poetry is meaningful to today's children. He speaks of the basic elements and emotions in life—love, hate, aspirations, despair; he writes in the language of today, and speaks for tomorrow.

Traveling around the country as a consultant to Bank Street College of Education's Harlem Center gave me the opportunity to read the work of Langston Hughes to students of various ages and backgrounds from kindergarten classrooms to college campuses. Included in this collection are those poems which evoked special feelings from young listeners and readers.

The title of this book, Don't You Turn Back, is taken from one of Langston Hughes' most poignant poems, *Mother to Son*:

> *So, boy, don't you turn back.*
> *Don't you set down on the steps*
> *'Cause you finds it kinder hard.*
> *Don't you fall now—*
> *For I'se still goin', honey,*
> *I'se still climbin*
> *And life for me ·ain't been no crystal stair.*

Lee Bennett Hopkins
July 10, 1969

MY PEOPLE

My People

The night is beautiful,
So the faces of my people.

The stars are beautiful,
So the eyes of my people.

Beautiful, also, is the sun.
Beautiful, also, are the souls of my people.

Aunt Sue's Stories

Aunt Sue has a head full of stories.
Aunt Sue has a whole heart full of stories.
Summer nights on the front porch
Aunt Sue cuddles a brown-faced child to her bosom
And tells him stories.

Black slaves
Working in the hot sun,
And black slaves
Walking in the dewy night,
And black slaves
Singing sorrow songs on the banks of a mighty river
Mingle themselves softly
In the flow of old Aunt Sue's voice,
Mingle themselves softly
In the dark shadows that cross and recross
Aunt Sue's stories.

And the dark-faced child, listening,
Knows that Aunt Sue's stories are real stories.
He knows that Aunt Sue never got her stories
Out of any book at all,
But that they came
Right out of her own life.

The dark-faced child is quiet
Of a summer night
Listening to Aunt Sue's stories.

Sun Song

Sun and softness,
Sun and the beaten hardness of the earth,
Sun and the song of all the sun-stars
Gathered together—
Dark ones of Africa,
I bring you my songs
To sing on the Georgia roads.

The Negro Speaks of Rivers

I've known rivers:
I've known rivers ancient as the world and older than the
    flow of human blood in human veins.

My soul has grown deep like the rivers.

I bathed in the Euphrates when dawns were young.
I built my hut near the Congo and it lulled me to sleep.
I looked upon the Nile and raised the pyramids above it.
I heard the singing of the Mississippi when Abe Lincoln
    went down to New Orleans, and I've seen its muddy
    bosom turn all golden in the sunset.

I've known rivers:
Ancient, dusky rivers.

My soul has grown deep like the rivers.

Mexican Market Woman

This ancient hag
Who sits upon the ground
Selling her scanty wares
Day in, day round,
Has known high wind-swept mountains,
And the sun has made
Her skin so brown.

Troubled Woman

She stands
In the quiet darkness,
This troubled woman
Bowed by
Weariness and pain
Like an
Autumn flower
In the frozen rain,
Like a
Wind-blown autumn flower
That never lifts its head
Again.

Baby

Albert!
Hey, Albert!
Don't you play in dat road.
   You see dem trucks
   A goin' by.
   One run ovah you
   An' you die.
Albert, don't you play in dat road.

April Rain Song

Let the rain kiss you.
Let the rain beat upon your head with silver liquid drops.
Let the rain sing you a lullaby.

The rain makes still pools on the sidewalk.
The rain makes running pools in the gutter.
The rain plays a little sleep-song on our roof at night—

And I love the rain.

Lullaby

(For a Black Mother)

My little dark baby,
My little earth-thing,
My little love-one,
What shall I sing
For your lullaby?

Stars,
Stars,
A necklace of stars
Winding the night.

My little black baby,
My dark body's baby,
What shall I sing
For your lullaby?

Moon,
Moon,
Great diamond moon,
Kissing the night.

Oh, little dark baby,
Night black baby,

Stars, stars,
Moon,
Night stars,
Moon,

For your sleep-song lullaby!

Hope

Sometimes when I'm lonely,
Don't know why,
Keep thinkin' I won't be lonely
By and by.

Mother to Son

Well, son, I'll tell you:
Life for me ain't been no crystal stair.
It's had tacks in it,
And splinters,
And boards torn up,
And places with no carpet on the floor—
Bare.
But all the time
I'se been a-climbin' on,
And reachin' landin's,
And turnin' corners,
And sometimes goin' in the dark
Where there ain't been no light.
So, boy, don't you turn back.
Don't you set down on the steps
'Cause you finds it kinder hard.
Don't you fall now—
For I'se still goin', honey,
I'se still climbin',
And life for me ain't been no crystal stair.

Ennui

It's such a
Bore
Being always
Poor.

Stars

O, sweep of stars over Harlem streets,
O, little breath of oblivion that is night.
  A city building
  To a mother's song.
  A city dreaming
  To a lullaby.
Reach up your hand, dark boy, and take a star.
Out of the little breath of oblivion
  That is night,
  Take just
  One star.

Alabama Earth

(At Booker Washington's grave)

Deep in Alabama earth
His buried body lies—
But higher than the singing pines
And taller than the skies
And out of Alabama earth
To all the world there goes
The truth a simple heart has held
And the strength a strong hand knows,
While over Alabama earth
These words are gently spoken:
Serve—and hate will die unborn.
Love—and chains are broken.

Poem

I loved my friend.
He went away from me.
There's nothing more to say.
The poem ends,
Soft as it began—
I loved my friend.

Youth

We have tomorrow
Bright before us
Like a flame.

Yesterday
A night-gone thing,
A sun-down name.

And dawn-today
Broad arch above the road we came.

We march!

Walkers with the Dawn

Being walkers with the dawn and morning,
Walkers with the sun and morning,
We are not afraid of night,
Nor days of gloom,
Nor darkness—
Being walkers with the sun and morning.

PRAYERS AND DREAMS

Prayer Meeting

Glory! Halleluiah!
De dawn's a-comin'!
Glory! Halleluiah!
De dawn's a-comin'!
A black old woman croons
In the amen-corner of the
Ebecanezer Baptist Church.
A black old woman croons—
De dawn's a-comin'!

Shout

Listen to yo' prophets,
　Little Jesus!
Listen to yo' saints!

Feet o' Jesus

At the feet o' Jesus,
Sorrow like a sea.
Lordy, let yo' mercy
Come driftin' down on me.

At the feet o' Jesus
At yo' feet I stand.
O, ma little Jesus,
Please reach out yo' hand.

Tambourines

Tambourines!
Tambourines!
Tambourines
To the glory of God!
Tambourines
To glory!

A gospel shout
And a gospel song:
Life is short
But God is long!

Tambourines!
Tambourines!
Tambourines
To glory!

Prayer

I ask you this:
Which way to go?
I ask you this:
Which sin to bear?
Which crown to put
Upon my hair?
I do not know,
Lord God,
I do not know.

Heaven

Heaven is
The place where
Happiness is
Everywhere.

Animals
And birds sing—
As does
Everything.

To each stone,
"How-do-you-do?"
Stone answers back,
"Well! And you?"

The Dream Keeper

Bring me all of your dreams,
You dreamers,
Bring me all of your
Heart melodies
That I may wrap them
In a blue cloud-cloth
Away from the too-rough fingers
Of the world.

Dream Variation

To fling my arms wide
In some place of the sun,
To whirl and to dance
Till the white day is done.
Then rest at cool evening
Beneath a tall tree
While night comes on gently,
    Dark like me—
That is my dream!

To fling my arms wide
In the face of the sun,
Dance! Whirl! Whirl!
Till the quick day is done.
Rest at pale evening . . .
A tall, slim tree . . .
Night coming tenderly
    Black like me.

Dream Dust

Gather out of star-dust
   Earth-dust,
   Cloud-dust,
   Storm-dust,
And splinters of hail,
One handful of dream-dust
   Not for sale.

Dreams

Hold fast to dreams
For if dreams die
Life is a broken-winged bird
That cannot fly.

Hold fast to dreams
For when dreams go
Life is a barren field
Frozen with snow.

Snail

Little snail,
Dreaming you go.
Weather and rose
Is all you know.

Weather and rose
Is all you see,
Drinking
The dewdrop's
Mystery.

OUT TO SEA

Long Trip

The sea is a wilderness of waves,
A desert of water.
We dip and dive,
Rise and roll,
Hide and are hidden
On the sea.
   Day, night,
   Night, day,
The sea is a desert of waves,
A wilderness of water.

Moonlight Night: Carmel

Tonight the waves march
In long ranks
Cutting the darkness
With their silver shanks,
Cutting the darkness
And kissing the moon
And beating the land's
Edge into a swoon.

Winter Moon

How thin and sharp is the moon tonight!
How thin and sharp and ghostly white
Is the slim curved crook of the moon tonight!

Sea Calm

How still,
How strangely still
The water is today.
It is not good
For water
To be so still that way.

Suicide's Note

The calm,
Cool face of the river
Asked me for a kiss.

Island

Wave of sorrow,
Do not drown me now:

I see the island
Still ahead somehow.

I see the island
And its sands are fair:

Wave of sorrow,
Take me there.

Wonder

Early blue evening.
Lights ain't come on yet.
   Looky yonder!
   They come on now!

Water-Front Streets

The spring is not so beautiful there—
    But dream ships sail away
To where the spring is wondrous rare
    And life is gay.

The spring is not so beautiful there—
    But lads put out to sea
Who carry beauties in their hearts
    And dreams, like me.

Sailor

He sat upon the rolling deck
Half a world away from home,
And smoked a Capstan cigarette
And watched the blue waves tipped with foam.

He had a mermaid on his arm,
An anchor on his breast,
And tattooed on his back he had
A blue bird in a nest.

Seascape

Off the coast of Ireland
As our ship passed by
We saw a line of fishing ships
Etched against the sky.

Off the coast of England
As we rode the foam
We saw an Indian merchantman
Coming home.

I AM A NEGRO

As I Grew Older

It was a long time ago.
I have almost forgotten my dream.
But it was there then,
In front of me,
Bright like a sun—
My dream.

And then the wall rose,
Rose slowly,
Slowly,
Between me and my dream.
Rose slowly, slowly,
Dimming,
Hiding,
The light of my dream.
Rose until it touched the sky—
The wall.

Shadow.
I am black.

I lie down in the shadow.
No longer the light of my dream before me,
Above me.

Only the thick wall.
Only the shadow.

My hands!
My dark hands!
Break through the wall!
Find my dream!
Help me to shatter this darkness,
To smash this night,

To break this shadow
Into a thousand lights of sun,
Into a thousand whirling dreams
Of sun!

The Negro

I am a Negro:
    Black as the night is black,
    Black like the depths of my Africa.

I've been a slave:
    Caesar told me to keep his door-steps clean.
    I brushed the boots of Washington.

I've been a worker:
    Under my hand the pyramids arose.
    I made mortar for the Woolworth Building.

I've been a singer:
    All the way from Africa to Georgia
    I carried my sorrow songs.
    I made ragtime.

I've been a victim:
    The Belgians cut off my hands in the Congo.
    They lynch me now in Texas.

I am a Negro:
    Black as the night is black.
    Black like the depths of my Africa.

Merry-Go-Round

Colored child at carnival:

Where is the Jim Crow section
On this merry-go-round,
Mister, cause I want to ride?
Down South where I come from
White and colored
Can't sit side by side.
Down South on the train
There's a Jim Crow car.
On the bus we're put in the back—
But there ain't no back
To a merry-go-round!
Where's the horse
For a kid that's black?

Color

Wear it
Like a banner
For the proud—
Not like a shroud.
Wear it
Like a song
Soaring high—
Not moan or cry.

I, Too

I, too, sing America.

I am the darker brother.
They send me to eat in the kitchen
When company comes,
But I laugh,
And eat well,
And grow strong.

Tomorrow,
I'll be at the table
When company comes.
Nobody'll dare
Say to me,
"Eat in the kitchen,"
Then.

Besides,
They'll see how beautiful I am
And be ashamed—

I, too, am America.

Brothers

We're related—you and I,
You from the West Indies,
I from Kentucky.

Kinsmen—you and I,
You from Africa,
I from the U.S.A.

Brothers—you and I.

Daybreak in Alabama

When I get to be a composer
I'm gonna write me some music about
Daybreak in Alabama
And I'm gonna put the purtiest songs in it
Rising out of the ground like a swamp mist
And falling out of heaven like soft dew.
I'm gonna put some tall trees in it
And the scent of pine needles
And the smell of red clay after rain
And long red necks
And poppy colored faces
And big brown arms
And the field daisy eyes
Of black and white black white black people
And I'm gonna put white hands
And black hands and brown and yellow hands
And red clay earth hands in it
Touching everybody with kind fingers
And touching each other natural as dew
In that dawn of music when I
Get to be a composer
And write about daybreak
In Alabama.

Index of Titles

Index of First Lines

About the Author

Langston Hughes devoted his life to writing and lecturing. Born in Joplin, Missouri, in 1902, he traveled throughout the world before making his home in Harlem. The poetry, song lyrics, essays, and short stories which he wrote, the plays, his autobiography, and his books for young people have been widely read in America and abroad.

Among the many awards he received were a Guggenheim Fellowship in 1935, a Rosenwald Fellowship in 1945, and a Spingarn Medal in 1960. In 1961 he was elected a member of the National Institute of Arts and Letters. Mr. Hughes died in 1967.

In *Black on White: A Critical Survey*, published in 1966, David Littlejohn wrote of Langston Hughes: "By moulding his verse always on the sounds of Negro talk, the rhythms of Negro music, by retaining his own keen honesty and directness, his poetic sense and ironic intelligence, he has maintained through four decades a readable newness distinctly his own."

LEE BENNETT HOPKINS is the author of several books and numerous articles appearing in *The Horn Book, Elementary English, Grade Teacher, Catholic School Journal, Negro History Bulletin,* and *The Instructor,* among other publications, a book reviewer, and an anthologist. He received his B.A. from Newark State College, an M.S. from Bank Street College of Education, and a Professional Diploma in Educational Supervision and Administration from Hunter College.

For three years, Mr. Hopkins directed a drama group for disadvantaged children in Newark, New Jersey, and from 1966 to 1968 he was coordinator of "Searchlight on Intelligence," a project in five schools in Harlem, New York. He has been an educational consultant in schools along the East Coast and in Texas and is an experienced lecturer on education. Presently Mr. Hopkins is Curriculum and Editorial Specialist for Scholastic, Inc. in New York.

While Lee Hopkins worked with inner-city children from Harlem schools, he discovered their special response to the poetry of Langston Hughes. As a result of his experience, he then selected the poems which were most meaningful to those children for inclusion in this book. The result is a collection which will have wide appeal to readers of many ages and backgrounds.

ANN GRIFALCONI shared the experiences of many city children while attending school in New York City. She has kept up a close relationship with young people by teaching in the same school system years later after attending Cooper Union Art School and Cincinnati and New York Universities for degrees in art and art education.

She is the author-illustrator of three books (*City Rhythms, The Toy Trumpet, and Camping Through Europe by Car*) and illustrator of more than 25 others, and her work has been cited by *The New York Times*, A.I.G.A., and the New York Public Library. Projects of special interest to Ann Grifalconi have included illustrating several poetry collections and two books on the history of African knowledge and the history of American Negroes. She has also enjoyed working on filmstrips, notably *Men of Thought, Men of Action* (a series on the black and white experience in American history), and a series on living poets. A very special feeling for woodcuts led her from the illustrations for *The Jazz Man* (1967 runner-up for the Newbery Medal) written by her mother, Mary H. Weik, through *The Ballad of the Burglar of Babylon* by Elizabeth Bishop to the present volume. Here her work has a simplicity, strength, and openness particularly suited to the moods and rhythms of the poetry of Langston Hughes.

Text set in Weiss
Composed by Westcott & Thomson, Inc., Philadelphia, Pa.
Printed by Rae Publishing Co., Cedar Grove, N.J.
Bound by Economy Bookbinding Corp., Kearny, N.J.
Typography by Atha Tebon